THE MONARCHY ROSE TO POWER ONCE AGAIN,

BRINGING SOCIAL COLLAPSE IN ITS WAKE. POLITICAL TURMOIL HAS LEFT MOST PEOPLE DESTITUTE AND DESPERATE.

MANY WHO CANNOT EARN AN HONEST LIVING TURN TO CRIME - AND PAY A STEEP PRICE FOR THEIR TRANSGRESSION.

YOU LIED TO US ABOUT YOUR ILLEGITIMATE DAUGHTER!

I'VE BEEN WORKING HERE FOR A YEAR NOW! YOU'VE NEVER HAD ANY COMPLAINTS!

I BEG YOU! PLEASE DON'T FIRE ME!

HERE, THE MAYOR IS GIVING YOU FIFTY FRANCS. LEAVE THE NEIGHBORHOOD!

GOOD THING I FOUND OUT ABOUT HER DAUGHTER FROM THE INNKEEPER IN MONTFERMIEL. THE MAYOR WOULD NEVER LET SUCH AN IMMORAL WOMAN KEEP WORKING HERE!

PLEASE, HEAR ME OUT! I HAVE DEBTS TO PAY! I NEED THIS JOB! I DON'T UNDERSTAND... WHAT HAVE I DONE WRONG...?

HOW AM I TO PAY FOR COSETTE NOW...?

NO MORE ARGUMENTS! YOU ARE DISMISSED!

SLAM

FWOOO~ FWOOO~

HOW AM I TO GET THAT MUCH MONEY...?

Winter is coming, and Cosette has outgrown all her clothes.

Send ten francs for a warm winter skirt.

~Thénardier

FWOOOSH~

NOW MY CHILD IS NO LONGER COLD...

... I HAVE DRESSED HER WITH MY HAIR.

I...

HAHAHA!

LOOK! SHE'S GOT NO HAIR!

HAHAHA!

HOW INDECENT!

HAHA!

HAHA!

DON'T WORRY, I HAVE AN IDEA ON HOW TO GET THE MONEY...

A FEW DAYS LATER, IN MONTREUIL-SUR-MER

NO... NOT MY TEETH...

YES, YOU! WHAT BEAUTIFUL TEETH YOU HAVE!

DO YOU WISH TO SELL ME YOUR TWO UPPER FRONT TEETH? I WILL GIVE YOU TWENTY FRANCS EACH FOR THEM.

I WISH I HAD TEETH TO SELL FOR TWENTY FRANCS!

YOU WON'T KEEP THEM FOREVER, ANYWAY!

MADAME, WHAT DO YOU KNOW ABOUT MILITARY FEVER?

MY HAIR WILL GROW BACK, MY TEETH WON'T...

BUT... COSETTE IS ILL...

HUFF~ HUFF~

OH MY! THAT IS A TERRIBLE DISEASE! CHILDREN MAY EASILY DIE WITHOUT THE RIGHT MEDICINE!

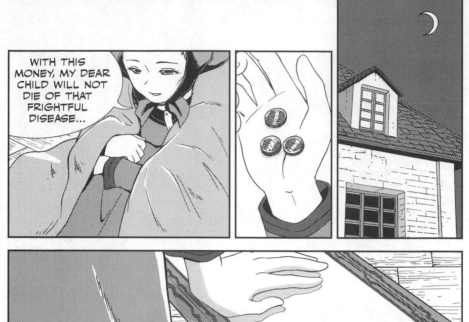

WITH THIS MONEY, MY DEAR CHILD WILL NOT DIE OF THAT FRIGHTFUL DISEASE...

KRASH!

WHAT HAVE I BECOME ???

SILENCE!

MAYOR MADELEINE, PERMIT ME...

DO NOT QUESTION ME FURTHER.

I AM SORRY FOR YOUR TROUBLES. I SWEAR, I DID NOT KNOW. BUT I SHALL MAKE AMENDS! YOUR CHILD WILL BE BROUGHT TO YOU, AND I WILL SETTLE ALL YOUR DEBTS.

AS YOU WISH...

CREAK!

IF ALL IS AS YOU SAY, AND I DO NOT DOUBT IT. YOU HAVE NEVER CEASED TO BE VIRTUOUS AND HOLY IN THE SIGHT OF GOD.

YOU SHALL BE HONEST AND HAPPY ONCE MORE.

I SHALL SEE MY CHILD AGAIN... THANK YOU!

FANTINE HAS BEEN SAVED BY THE POWERFUL MAYOR MADELEINE! BUT WHO IS THIS MYSTERIOUS STRANGER AND WHAT IS HIS TRAGIC TALE? WILL COSETTE SURVIVE THE CRUELTY OF THE THÉNADIERS? AND HOW WILL INSPECTOR JAVERT RESPOND TO MAYOR MADELIENE'S DEFIANCE? FOR THE COMPLETE STORY OF VICTOR HUGO'S UNFORGETTABLE CHARACTERS, VISIT YOUR COMIC BOOK SHOP IN AUGUST FOR UDON'S MANGA CLASSICS –

Les Misérables

Les Misérables

Victor Hugo

Adapted for stage and screen, loved by millions, Victor Hugo's classic novel of love & tragedy set in 19th Century France is reborn in this fantastic new manga edition! Gorgeous and expressive art brings to life the unforgettable stories of Jean Valjean, Inspector Javert, and the tragic Fantine, in this epic adaptation of "*Les Misérables*!"

Art by: SunNeko Lee
Adapted by: Crystal Silvermoon & Stacy King

8.25 inches X 5.75 inches
336 Pages / Black & White

Hard Cover Version - Cover Price: US$24.99
ISBN: 978-1-927925-15-7

Soft Cover Version - Cover Price: US$19.99
ISBN: 978-1-927925-16-4

 An UDON Entertainment Production, in association with Morpheus Animation Studios.

www.udonentertainment.com
www.morpheusanimation.com
©UDON Entertainment Corp. All Rights Reserved.

CLASSIC STORIES, MODERN MANGA!

Elizabeth (Lizzy) Bennet

Pride and Prejudice

Jane Austen

Art by: Po Tse
Story Adaptation by:
Stacy King

MangaClassics.com

MangaClassics.com

UDON Entertainment proudly presents: **Manga Classics!**
The finest name in adaptations of great, classic literature!

UDON is proud to bring you this very special new line of books, adapting classic literature with the same attention to detail and quality as our fantastic graphic novels, art books, and manga releases! UDON's Manga Classics is an international partnership with Asian comics and animation studio Morpheus, to bring the highest-quality adaptations of these works to the North American market!

UDON and Morpheus have worked very hard to fully realize the world of these classic works of literature. The artists have done extensive research on the settings of these works, to give the costumes and architecture a real weight and accuracy, expertly executed thanks to the studio's animation background. This high quality work has been coupled with a generous page count of over 350 pages per book, more than double the average comics-format adaptation! This allows for a more thorough, accurate, and natural adaptation of the source material, with the artists' vision given as much space as it needs to be properly realized. In short, these look and read like great commercial manga, while being faithful adaptations of literary classics!

Intended for a young adult audience, UDON's Manga Classics are just as likely to be enjoyed in the reader's free time as in the classroom. The gripping and intense story of Les Misérables and the lush shoujo art of Pride and Prejudice place them easily alongside today's bestselling popular manga, with strong and accurate adaptations that will please even the toughest teacher or librarian! UDON's Manga Classics are also a great way for adult readers to rediscover their favourite classics, or experience them for the first time!

<Right>: Character Design Sketches of Mr. Darcy and Elizabeth from Pride & Prejudice.

Turn the page to read a preview of Jane Austen's Pride & Prejudice

Pride & Prejudice
Jane Austen

SPECIAL PREVIEW

Art by: Po Tse   Story Adapted by: Stacy King

JANE AND ELIZABETH.

...

OH, I'M SURE WE WILL!

RIGHT, DARCY...?

I DO HOPE YOU'LL ENJOY YOURSELVES THIS EVENING.